Stephen Mackey

Miki

and the Moon Blossom

Hodder
Children's
Books

A DIVISION OF HACHETTE CHILDREN'S BOOKS

Long ago and far away in a land of ice
and snow there lived a little girl called Miki.

One morning, she and her friends Polar Bear
and Penguin were hanging out the washing.
'There!' said Miki. 'I wish there was
a breeze to make it all dry.'

Just then, the wind started to blow. Everything whirled into the air and Polar Bear grabbed at a strange spiky thing as it flew past.

'Just what we need to hold up the washing,' he said,
sticking it in the ground.

That night, while Miki was fast asleep, something very strange
was happening. The spiky thing began to grow. It was a seed!

As Miki slept on, it grew and grew.

Little tendrils curled round her house and gently lifted it into the air.

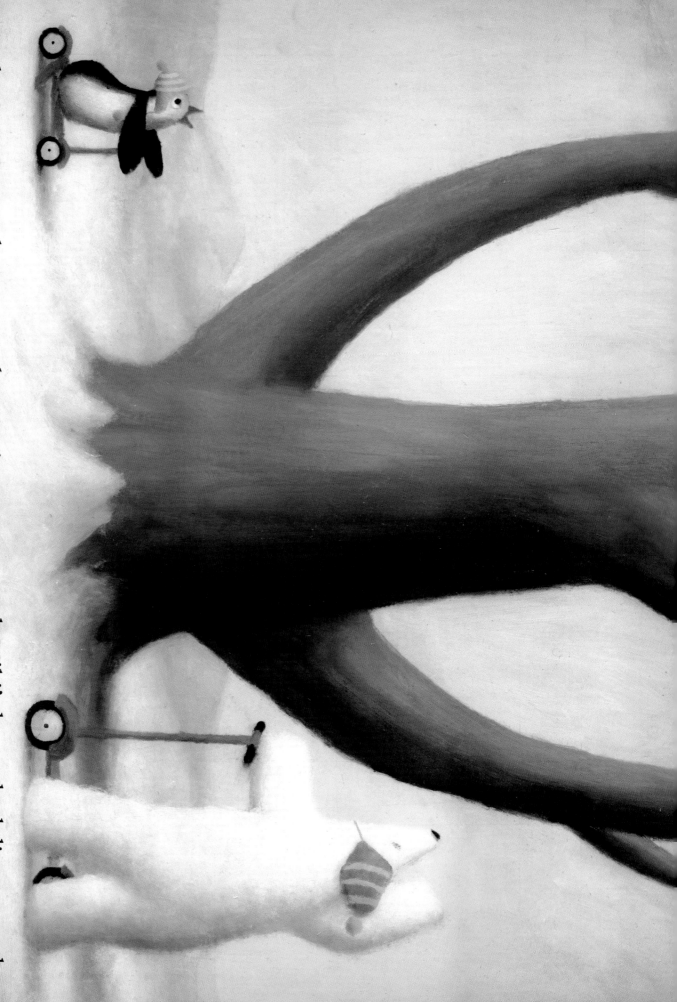

In the morning, Polar Bear and Penguin were amazed. Miki's house had disappeared and she was nowhere to be seen. 'Where are you?' they cried. Way up in the air, far above them, a tiny voice answered, 'I'm up here!'

'We're coming!' said Polar Bear, and he and Penguin scrambled onto the enormous plant and started to climb. Up and up and up.

'Oh, I'm scared of heights!' squeaked Penguin.
'Get on my back,' offered Polar Bear.

Way above them, Miki ran out on to the stem of the gigantic plant. The air was warm and heavy with the scent of flowers.

'Which way is down?'
said Miki aloud.
She had the strangest
feeling that someone
was watching her.

Sure enough, little faces were peeping out
from one of the huge flowers.
'I wish you'd help me find
my friends!' said Miki.
Just then, a little breeze ruffled
the gorgeous blossoms.

The wind was blowing harder as Polar Bear
and Penguin reached Miki's little house.
'Miki!' cried Polar Bear, looking inside.
'Where are you?'

Penguin had spotted Miki riding on the back of a strange creature.
'There she is!' he cried. 'Give her back at once!'
But the creature flew away over the clouds, and Penguin
and Polar Bear ran after it.

As they reached the top of the flower, they saw a sailing ship,
dipping and rolling in the gusting wind.
Miki was running towards them.

"I'm so happy
to find you,'
she cried.
'These creatures are our friends!
There's a terrible storm coming and
they're helping us to escape. Hurry!'

The three friends scrambled aboard the ship just in time.
A tremendous blast of wind shook them into the stormy sky and ripped
the gigantic plant to pieces. The air was full of flying flowers and seeds

By sunset, the wind was quieter and the ship sailed more calmly
through the sky.

'We'd better be going back home,' said Miki.

'But how?' grumbled Penguin.

The ship gave a little shiver. Then it started drifting downwards.

Miki, Penguin and Polar Bear held hands and jumped
out into the snow.

The huge plant was now nothing but a broken
stalk and, above them, the ship was disappearing into the clouds.

Miki cried out, 'I'll miss you! I wish we could see you again.' A little breeze whispered over the icy land.

'Look!' cried Penguin, and Miki and Polar Bear stared into the distance...

There, in the moonlight, were hundreds of plants, uncurling their
lovely leaves in the snow and, as the friends watched,
they grew taller and taller towards the sky...
Miki's icy world had never looked so beautiful.

FOR HELEN

FIRST PUBLISHED IN HARDBACK IN 2010 BY HODDER CHILDREN'S BOOKS
FIRST PUBLISHED IN PAPERBACK IN 2011
COPYRIGHT © STEPHEN MACKEY 2010

WWW.STEPHENMACKEY.COM

HODDER CHILDREN'S BOOKS, 338 EUSTON ROAD, LONDON, NW1 3BH
HODDER CHILDREN'S BOOKS AUSTRALIA, LEVEL 17/207 KENT STREET, SYDNEY, NSW 2000

HB ISBN 978 0 340 95066 1
PB ISBN 978 0 340 95067 8

PRINTED IN CHINA

HODDER CHILDREN'S BOOKS IS A DIVISION OF HACHETTE CHILDREN'S BOOKS,
AN HACHETTE UK COMPANY

WWW.HACHETTE.CO.UK